Featuring

TOMB RAIDER™

Ceremony

WITCHBLADE™ **featuring TOMB RAIDER**™: **CEREMONY**

ISBN 1 84023 093 2

Published by

Titan Books Ltd

42 - 44 Dolben St

London SE1 0UP

In association with Top Cow Productions, Inc.

This book collects *Witchblade* #5–8 and *Witchblade/Tomb Raider Special* #1.

A CIP catalogue record for this title is available from the British Library.

First edition: October 1999

10 9 8 7 6 5 4 3 2 1

Printed in Italy.

WITCHBLADE

FEATURING

TOMB RAIDER

CEREMONY

TITAN BOOKS

IN ASSOCIATION WITH
TOP COW PRODUCTIONS, INC.

ACTION ON BOTH fRONTS!

Once more into the breach, action-fans, as we nosedive into another full-throttle feast of mayhem and mysticism, courtesy of Lara Croft, the Tomb Raider, and Sara Pezzini, Witchblade. First off, it's team-up time, as Lara and Sara pit their collective wits against an all-powerful lion goddess, a catfight destined to raise more than just a few hackles. Last time out (see *Witchblade featuring Tomb Raider: Covenant*, also available from Titan Books), the double-barrelled duo found themselves embroiled in a series of killings, perpetrated by a winged demon. That life and death struggle forged a deep bond between them, one that is now renewed — and how! Stand well back, take cover, and get ready for Tomb Raider/Witchblade, Round Two! And, as if that wasn't enough, more intimate secrets from Sara Pezzini's early days as owner of the Witchblade are laid bare, as she fights to master both the mystic artefact itself and those who wish to claim its power for themselves. Phew!

But first, let's meet the ladies...

LARA CROFT, the TOMB RAIDER. Free-spirited and beholden to no one, multi-millionaire archaeologist Lara Croft traverses the world in search of action, adventure and long-lost treasure. As a girl, Lara survived a plane crash that killed both of her parents. That brush with death left her forever unsatisfied with the quiet life, and now Lara craves the constant adrenaline rush that comes from poking her nose in some very dark, musty corners of the globe. Put simply, Lara's not living unless she's facing death. Whatever the menace to society, Lara's not afraid to hand out 9mm justice.

SARA PEZZINI, a NYPD homicide detective, discovers a mystical gauntlet known as the WITCHBLADE, a living weapon that melds with her psyche, judging her to be worthy of its power. But though the Witchblade saves Sara's life several times, she initially fears its power, unable to rein in the sheer destructive force she now possesses. Others, though, covet its power, chief among them Kenneth Irons, a multi-millionaire tycoon obsessed with possessing the Witchblade, or whoever wears it, at all costs. Irons' righthand man, Ian Nottingham, a lethal living weapon himself, now makes his move...

Volume Two in Titan's bestselling Witchblade/Tomb Raider series picks up where Volume One left off, and then cranks up the action quotient a full hundred per cent. Get ready to rumble...

...BUT I DIDN'T SEE ANY MORE REFERENCES TO IT BEFORE BUCK AND I REACHED THE SHRINE.
THE PLACE WAS SIMPLY...
...BREATH-TAKING. WHAT MAKES THE LIGHT, DO YOU SUPPOSE?
THE ANCIENT EGYPTIANS WERE STUDENTS OF MAGIC. PERHAPS SOME LOST MYSTICAL TECHNIQUE...?
LARA, DID YOU SEE THIS? THE DETAIL ON THESE STATUES IS UNREAL.
THANK GOD NO GRAVE ROBBERS EVER FOUND THIS PLACE.
ALL RIGHT, HERE GOES.
I'VE GOT IT. IT'S HEAVY...
...AND ...UMM...IT'S EYES ARE GLOWING...
UH...LARA, THESE STATUES ARE MOVING.
I THINK WE'D BETTER GET OUT OF HERE!

THAT IS EASILY ACCOMPLISHED.

WHAT?! AAHHH!

MAYBE THEY'VE GOT THE RIGHT IDEA.

YOU KNOW WE CAN'T DO THAT. THIS MESS IS MY RESPONSIBILITY. AND SINCE WE CAN'T PROSECUTE A CAT FOR HOMICIDE--

OR A GODDESS...

--THE PLAN IS SIMPLE. WE'VE GOT TO PUT BASTET BACK INTO THE IDOL, FOR STARTERS...

MANARES?

...LET'S GET HER ATTENTION.

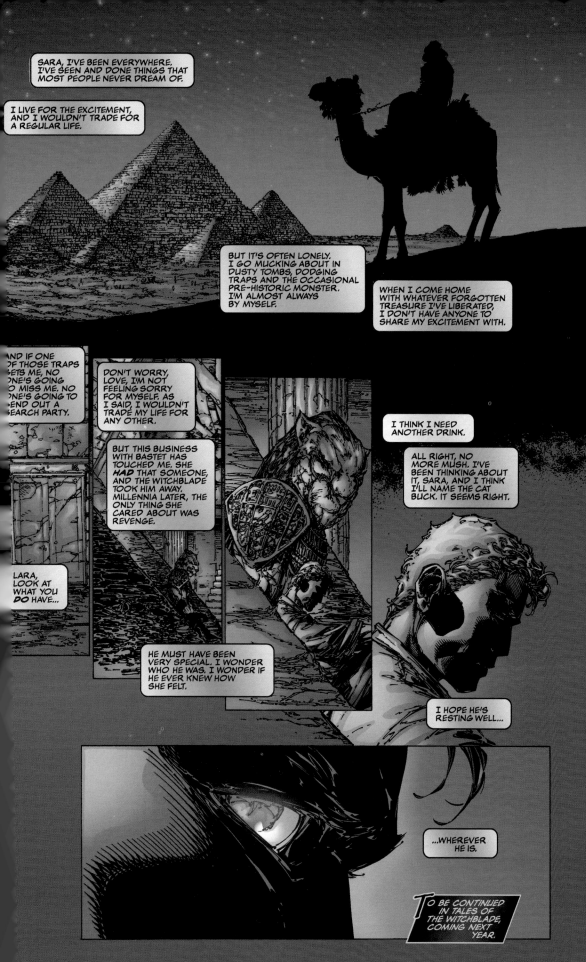

FROM AN OUTSIDER'S POINT OF VIEW, IT SEEMED SO **NORMAL.**

MORNING IN MANHATTAN. A GIRL SLEEPING IN A GUY'S BED. **JAKE'S BED.**

FUNNY. IT **DID** SEEM NORMAL. BUT SOMETHING VERY **ABNORMAL** HAPPENED WHILE I SLEPT.

I KEEP GOING OVER IT IN MY MIND. IF I TRY TO CONCENTRATE ON IT FOR VERY LONG, THE FEELING DISAPPEARS.

A FEELING I HAD WHILE I WAS SLEEPING--LIKE A DREAM. IT FELT **TOO** REAL.

WHAT AM I SAYING? IT **WAS** REAL.

I FELT **IT** ON ME, LIKE SOME PROTECTIVE SHELL. AND THE WEIRD THING IS--IT FELT **RIGHT** ON ME. AND I DIDN'T WANT TO WAKE UP BECAUSE IT FELT SO GOOD...SO **SAFE.**

AS I LAY THERE, SLOWLY COMING OUT OF MY SLEEP, MY MIND BEGAN ITS DAILY ROUTINE OF SORTING OUT THE STUFF FROM THE PREVIOUS DAY.

AND WHAT IT SORTED WAS NEITHER **NORMAL** NOR **SAFE.**

I KNOW **HOMICIDE** DETECTIVES AREN'T KNOWN FOR HAVING REGULAR LIVES, BUT THIS WAS PRETTY CRAZY--EVEN BY **OUR** STANDARDS.

I COULD SEE MYSELF WRITING IT UP ON A **STATUS REPORT:**

Attempted to bring Yee, my old partner, back to life with glove that was EXHIBIT C at the Rialto disaster, threw the glove in the coroner's incinerator and proceeded to Better Bodies gym to work off some frustration...

I'D GO ON TO WRITE THAT...

While there, I met an interesting man, KEN, and upon my departure, was KIDNAPPED by high-end thugs, taken aboard a YACHT and forced to put on the glove that SOMEHOW ended up in THEIR hands.

CHIEF SIRY'D BE READING IN **DISBELIEF,** ESPECIALLY WHEN HE CAME TO MY NOTES ABOUT...

the man wielding a BROADSW who was the very person who K!!!ED my pa at the Rialto.

And like me, he'd be SUSPICIOUS about Ken arriving on Liberty Island at the moment of my near-demise.

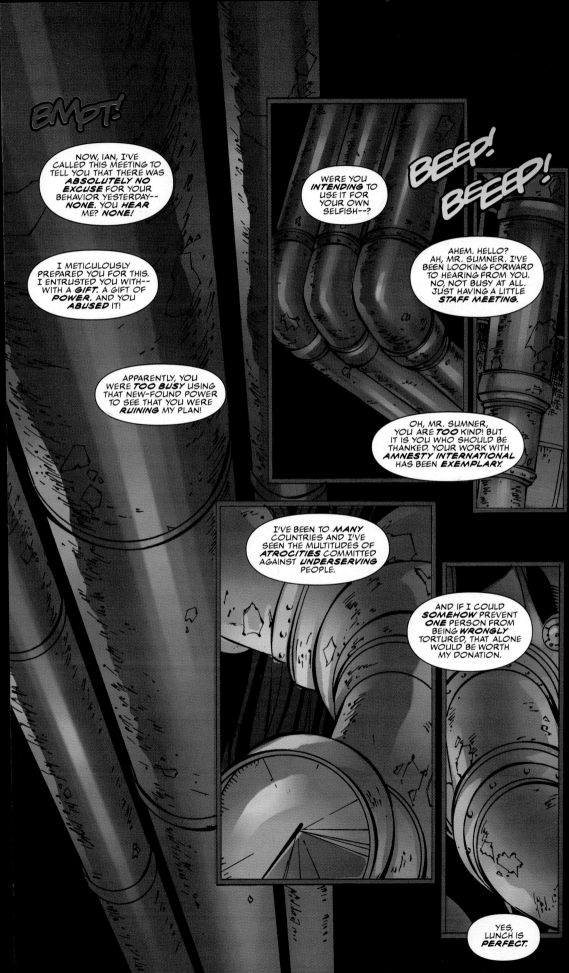

4:10 P.M., SAME BUILDING.

YOU CERTAINLY ARE AN INTERESTING MAN, KEN.

SO IT WAS YOU WHO SENT ME THE FLOWERS

IRON'S INTERNATIONAL INVESTMENT & HOLDINGS. I SEE.

WELL...MR. IRONS...YOU S TO KNOW SO MUCH ABO ME, I WANT TO LEARN W YOU'RE ABOUT.

IRON'S INTERNATIONAL INVESTMENT & HOLDINGS, PLEASE HOLD.

IRON'S INTER-- DAVEN! HOLD A SEC, I'VE GOT TWO CONFERENCE CALLS TO PATCH INTO MR. IRONS.

NO, I TOLD YOU I'M WORKING THROUGH LUNCH. HE'S HAVING THIS HUGE MEETING--A VERY LARGE DEAL. OKAY, BYE.

WELL, THIS CERTAINLY ISN'T WHERE THE OFFICE ACTION IS.

AH, HERE WE GO.

MR. NOTTINGHAM, MR. IRONS TOLD ME YOU HAVE SOME OF THE RAREST JAPANESE SWORDS ON THIS EARTH. HE SAID YOU MIGHT SHOW ME--

--OH, HE DID, DID HE?

THERE REALLY IS NO SUCH THING AS A "SECURED" FLOOR.

REGULATION FIRE EXITS ARE SUPPOSED TO HAVE "STOREROOM" LOCKS INSTALLED SO THAT YOU CAN ONLY GO THROUGH A DOOR ONE WAY, AND NOT REENTER--

3:25 A.M.

THE P.I.'S RESOURCE DEPARTMENT'S A PRETTY DEAD PLACE THESE DAYS. IT'S EASIER TO HAND SOME BUM A **FIVE DOLLAR BILL** THAN TO BANG ON A COMPUTER.

MOST OF THE INFO IN THESE COMPUTERS AREN'T WORTH A DAMN WHEN DEALING WITH 16 YEAR OLD MURDERERS.

BUT, THEY **ARE** GOOD FOR FINDING INFORMATION ABOUT A PERSON WHO IS **PROMINENT** ENOUGH TO HAVE A PUBLIC FILE.

HEY, COOPER. OH, NOTHING MUCH. JUST WORKING. OH, I HAVE SOMETHING YOU'D BE INTERESTED IN--MY SISTER JUST LEFT ME A MESSAGE TELLING ME SHE'S FLYING IN FOR A LITTLE STAY. YOU AND HER HIT IT OFF LAST TIME, DIDN'T YOU?

YOU KNOW, COOP, I CAN'T BE HELD RESPONSIBLE FOR HER. JUST BECAUSE SHE LEFT YOU STRANDED IN BROOKLYN WITH YOUR PANTS DOWN, DOESN'T MEAN IT'S MY FAULT. HAHA.

BUT, BACK TO BUSINESS. WHAT'D YOU FIND? NOTHING? ARE YOU SURE? WHAT ABOUT LISTED UNDER JUST IRONS INTERNATIONAL? YOU'RE KIDDING! HE'S SQUEAKY CLEAN?

LOOK, DON'T GO OFF ON ME. I NEVER REALLY PAID ATTENTION TO HIM. YOU KNOW I DON'T WATCH TV.

THE NEWS? COOP, MY JOB DOESN'T AFFORD ME THE LUXURY TO HEAR WATERED-DOWN, SENSATIONALISTIC CRAP. YEAH, YEAH. BYE.

Irons, Ke
Irons' Interna
Investments &
575 Madison Av
New York, NY
Offices: New York, Lor
Buenos Aires,
Cairo, Los An
Sydney, Hon

SIC #8908-0998 Prima
Assets worth: Over 200 Bill
If you are reading type this must
you really need to get a hobby.
Witchblade rules Mike Turner
the Bomb! D-Tron & my idol.

KENNETH IRONS. YOU REALLY WANT TO BUY **ME** COFFEE?

GOD, IT'S BEEN A LONG DAY...

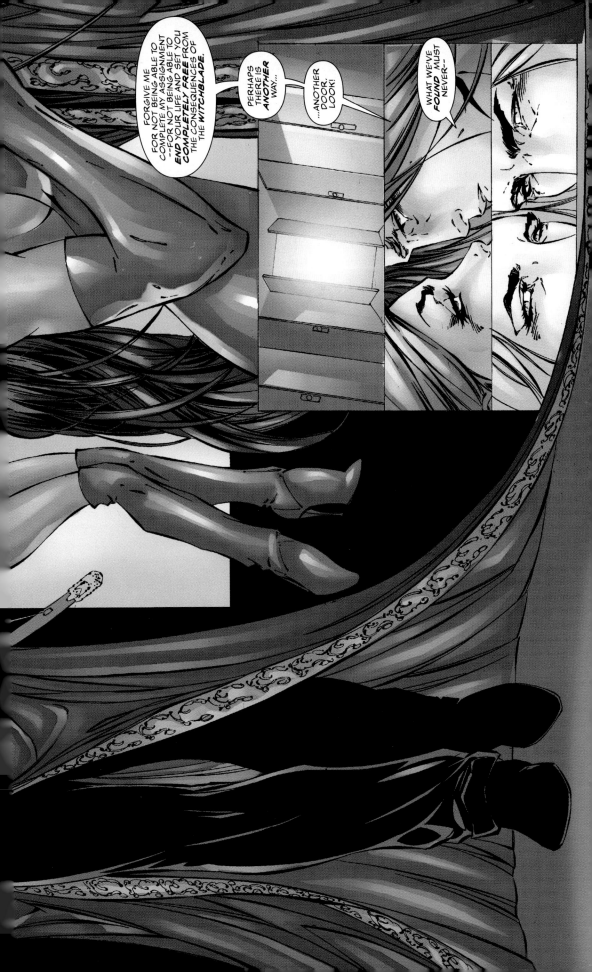

IT'S SUCH A BEAUTIFUL DAY. LIKE YOU'RE NOT EVEN DEAD.

MOST OF THESE GUYS--AS SOON AS THEY GET OUT OF HERE, THEY'RE GONNA FIRE UP THE BARBECUE, TAKE THE KIDS TO THE PARK.

LIKE YOU'RE NOT EVEN GONE.

MICHAEL. I DON'T WANT TO LET YOU GO. MAYBE I *SHOULD* HAVE SEEN THE GRIEVANCE COUNSELOR. MAYBE I JUST REALLY NEEDED TO TAKE SOME TIME AND MOURN LIKE *REAL* PEOPLE DO.

HARD TO NOT BE PREOCCUPIED WITH THE OTHER STUFF THAT'S BEEN GOING ON: THE DREAM, KEN IRONS, THIS...*THING* ON MY WRIST.

THE DREAM...HE CALLED IT...THE *WITCHBLADE*.

AND WHILE I'M HEADING MY OWN PERSONAL INVESTIGATION, THE MAN WHO ORDERED YOUR DEATH IS STILL OUT THERE. I KNOW, BECAUSE HE NEARLY *KILLED* ME!

SO, HERE I AM, BLINKING BACK TEARS SO NO ONE WILL SEE ME CRY. AND IF I DID, WOULD THESE TEARS BE ONLY FOR YOU, MICHAEL? WOULD THEY BE BECAUSE I KNOW YOU'LL NEVER SEE YOUR DAUGHTER GROW UP?

OR DO YOU SUPPOSE IT WOULD BE FOR EVERYTHING THAT'S HAPPENED TO ME THESE PAST FEW DAYS.

AND HERE, YOUR FAMILY MOURNS YOU PROPERLY. WITH TEARS AND SOBS. WHY AM I SO CONCERNED WITH BEING COMPOSED AND NOBLE ABOUT THIS?

PART OF ME WANTS TO BREAK DOWN AND THE OTHER PART WANTS TO BE LIKE STEEL--SO THAT *NOTHING* CAN GET TO ME.

BUT MICHAEL, I'M STAYING **STRONG** FOR YOU. YOU WOULD'VE WANTED IT THAT WAY. TO ACT-- LIKE YOU'RE NOT EVEN DEAD.

GOD KNOWS I'LL **HAVE** TO.

SELZER. FOR CHRISSAKES, WHAT'S IT GONNA BE **THIS** TIME.

WELL, **DE**-TECTIVE PEZZINI.

YOU'RE LOOKING IN FINE HEALTH. YOU **MUST** TELL ME YOUR REJUVENATION SECRETS! MAYBE YOU SHOULD'VE TRIED SOME OUT ON YOUR **PARTNER.**

SELZER, GET OUTTA MY FACE--

HOW YA DOING, KIDDO?

PEZ!

SARA, I'M ALWAYS AVAILABLE IF YOU WANT TO TALK ABOUT **ANYTHING.** YOU KNOW MY NUMBER. DALIA MISSES YOUR LATE-NIGHT CALLS, ANYWAY.

THANKS, CHIEF.

--SHE'S STILL OFFICIALLY ON **LEAVE,** SELZER. STOW THE QUESTIONS A WHILE.

JOE SIRY. ALWAYS THERE FOR ME.

NICE **OUTFIT,** HUH.

NOT QUITE AS HOT AS WHAT SHE WORE TO THE **RIALTO,** BUT STILL NICE.

WHATEVER.

I'M GONNA WALK FOR A WHILE, JOE. MAYBE CATCH A CAB. THAT LIMO'S KINDA DEPRESSING.

SURE... TAKE IT EASY.

WHERE AM I GOING?

FOR SOME REASON, I THOUGHT WALKING A FEW BLOCKS WOULD **MIRACULOUSLY** PUT MY LIFE IN ORDER.

SURPRISE. IT DIDN'T.

GOT TO RETRACE MY STEPS, RETHINK MY SITUATION. START ACTING LIKE A **COP** AGAIN. SOMETHING I HAVEN'T DONE FOR A WHILE.

FUNNY. BACK WHEN I WAS IN THE ACADEMY, A PSYCHOLOGIST THERE TOLD ME I WAS ONE OF THE MORE "TOGETHER" PEOPLE HE'D INTERVIEWED. HE ASKED IF I **REALLY** WANTED TO GET INTO HOMICIDE.

HE FIGURED I'D GET **DESENSITIZED** LIKE MOST OF THE DETECTIVES AROUND HERE. SOME OF THOSE GUYS COULD MAKE A JOKE WHEN THEY SEE A YOUNG BOY BLOW A HOLE IN HIS MOTHER FOR FOOD STAMPS. IT'S NOT SUPPOSED TO GET ME DOWN. BUT IT **DOES.**

HOW PEOPLE HAVE SUCH DISREGARD FOR HUMAN LIFE WILL FOREVER BE A MYSTERY TO ME. AND THOSE ARE THE **GOOD** GUYS.

AND MY DREAM. WHAT DID IT MEAN? THE MAN WITH THE SWORD. THOSE VERY HANDS THAT IN REALITY, HURT ME--WERE IN MY DREAM STATE, CARESSING ME.

OH DAMN. IT'S THE 10TH AND I STILL HAVEN'T PAID MY RENT. **DAMMIT.**

SIGH...

HOW 'BOUT THAT COFFEE, SARA?

I KNOW THAT VOICE.

I KNOW WHO I'M GOING TO SEE WHEN I LOOK UP.

IT'S **HIM.**

CENTRAL PARK WEST. 2:20 P.M.

GOOD AFTERNOON, SIR.

JEROME'S MY DOORMAN, ANYTIME YOU WANT TO LEAVE, JUST SAY THE WORD.

IT'S HAPPENING.

EVEN THOUGH HE'S GONE OVER THIS IN HIS MIND THOUSANDS OF TIMES, HE STILL CAN'T BELIEVE IT'S REALLY HAPPENING.

IT'S SO EXHILARATING, WISHING HE COULD TELL HER THE PLAN. JUST A LITTLE HINT. BUT NO-- IT'S NOT TIME YET.

HMM. WHERE TO BEGIN...ALL RIGHT...LONG BEFORE I BECAME A BUSINESSMAN, I WORKED WITH MY FATHER, A REKNOWNED ARCHEOLOGIST, IN EGYPT. TOGETHER WE WENT ON EXPEDITION AFTER EXPEDITION.

AS A PROFESSOR AT THE UNIVERSITY OF CAIRO HE UNCOVERED MANY RARE ARTIFACTS AND A NUMBER OF MYSTERIES THAT MANKIND STILL REJECTS.

IT WAS THERE THAT WE FIRST LEARNED OF THE WITCHBLADE. THE NAME COMES FROM SEVERAL TRANSLATIONS AND HAS VERY LITTLE TO DO WITH WITCHCRAFT OR ANY- THING OF THAT SORT.

AND, AS YOU WILL SEE, IT IS MOST LIKELY CONNECTED TO A NUMBER OF HISTORIC EVENTS WHERE THE SUPERNATURAL OCCURED.

I LIKE TO THINK OF MYSELF AS WELL EDUCATED, KEN. BUT I HAVE NEVER HEARD OF ANYTHING LIKE THIS. HOW DO YOU KNOW--

I DON'T, NOT EXACTLY. BUT I HAVE COLLECTED MANY ARTIFACTS AND DOCUMENTS THAT SUGGEST WE WERE RIGHT. COME, LET ME SHOW YOU THE SMALL EXHIBIT I KEEP HERE AT MY HOUSE. PERHAPS YOU MIGHT SEE SOME SIMILARITIES.

THE HELL WITH EXPLANATIONS, HE THINKS. THE WITCHBLADE IS SO CLOSE TO BEING HIS. WHY NOT JUST DO IT?

NO. SAVOR THE MOMENT. THEY'LL SHARE A LIFETIME TOGETHER. HE AND THE WITCHBLADE.

MY FATHER AND HIS CLOSEST ASSOCIATES BELIEVED THE WITCHBLADE TO BE AN ITEM THAT IS NOT OF SOME MAGICAL MAKE UP, BUT RATHER, AN EXTRATERRESTRIAL ITEM.

IN THE SIMPLEST TERMS, WE DON'T KNOW WHERE IT COMES FROM. BUT AFTER MY FATHER DIED IN A CAVE ACCIDENT, I TOOK OVER HIS SEARCH. IT IS WHAT I SPENT MUCH OF MY LIFE DOING UNTIL I FINALLY FOUND IT DURING AN EXCAVATION IN GREECE.

OH MY GOD.

JOAN OF ARC? HEARING VOICES. OH, GOD.

THIS IS ALL INCREDIBLE. BUT HOW DOES THIS TIE IN TO WHY YOU WERE AT LIBERTY ISLAND. PLEASE EXPLAIN THAT TO ME.

NO! SHE RUINED THE MOMENT! IRONS WISHES HE COULD HIT HER--FOR DESECRATING THIS ROOM WITH MEANINGLESS CHATTER. BUT STRIKING HER WOULD BE COUNTERPRODUCTIVE.

UNBELIEVABLE, HE THINKS, HERE IN THE CHAMBER DEVOTED TO THE WITCHBLADE, WALKS ITS PRESENT WIELDER. HOW DIVINELY PRECIOUS.

JOAN OF ARC. A SAINT CLAIMING TO HEAR VOICES, URGING HER TO FIGHT AGAINST SEEMINGLY INSUR-MOUNTABLE ODDS DURING THE HUNDRED YEARS WAR.

IT IS WRITTEN, HER SWORD SEEMINGLY CAME TO LIFE DURING HER BATTLES, AND AFTER HER CAPTURE AT COMPIEGNE, HER WEAPON DISAPPEARED FROM HER HAND.

CURIOUSLY, SHE WAS ONLY VULNERABLE WITHOUT IT. NO ONE KNOWS WHY SHE ABANDONED IT. MAYBE TRUE MARTYRDOM. WE'LL NEVER KNOW.

IRONS KNOWS THAT SARA WILL NEVER ABANDON THE WITCHBLADE. HE'LL MAKE SURE OF THAT.

:AHRM: WELL, IAN NOTTINGHAM AND MYSELF USED TO BE CO-WORKERS ON A JOURNEY THAT TOOK US TO DELHI. HE AND I BOTH WERE VERSED IN THE WITCHBLADE.

WHILE I WANTED TO FIND THE RIGHTFUL OWNER AND EDUCATE THEM, NOTTINGH[AM] WANTED TO USE THE POWER F[OR] HIS OWN SELFISH PURPOSES. IS RECENTLY HERE FROM TH[E] BRITISH ISLES AND I HA[VE] BE[EN] WATCHING HIM CAREFULLY.

I KNEW OF HIS TOURNAMENT AT THE RI[TZ] THEATER AND I HONES[TLY] DIDN'T THINK HE'D TRAIL [YOU] SO CLOSELY AND INTEN[D TO] DO YOU SUCH DAMAG[E. I] CERTAINLY COULDN'T [LET] YOU GET HURT, SO [I] INTERVENED.

IT ONLY HAS ONE OWNER OVER A GIVEN PERIOD OF TIME. ANYONE ELSE WHO TRIES TO POSSESS IT, SHALL PERISH.

SARA, WHETHER YOU LIKE IT OR NOT-- YOU ARE A CHANGED PERSON. IT'S UP TO YOU TO DECIDE WHETHER THIS IS A LIFE YOU WANT TO LEAD.

I CAN HELP YOU DEAL WITH IT OR HELP YOU REMOVE IT.

I KNOW WHAT HAPPENED AT THE RIALTO.

I WILL ABIDE BY ANY DECISION YOU CHOOSE.

YES HE WILL, AS LONG AS IT'S THE RIGHT ONE.

OH, IF ONLY THIS COARSE POLICE WOMAN COULD TRULY ENJOY WHAT IS HAPPENING.

HE CAN'T TAKE MUCH MORE.

TIME TO BEGIN.

THEY COULD LAUGH AND SHARE A COGNAC BEFORE THEY BEGAN THE PROCEDURE.

BUT NO, SHE'S NOT THE TYPE TO APPRECIATE SUCH FINERIES.

PLEASE, FEEL FREE TO LOOK AROUND. ALL OF THIS IS NOW A CONNECTION. A CONNECTION TO YOU.

HMM? WHAT A BEAUTIFUL TAPESTRY.

YES, HE SECRETLY IMPLORES HER-- GO THROUGH THE DOOR. GO ON. LET IT BEGIN RIGHT HERE, RIGHT NOW.

BUT THEN THE BUSINESSMAN IN HIM TAKES OVER. IT IS NOT THE RIGHT TIME. HE MUST BE PATIENT. HE'S WAITED OVER 80 YEARS FOR THIS MOMENT. WHAT'S ANOTHER COUPLE DAYS?

I'M SORRY, MISS PEZZINI. BUT I HAVE A MEETING I MUST ATTEND TO. I'LL SHOW YOU TO THE DOOR.

TO BE
CONTINUED...

CENTRAL PARK. 8:10 P.M.

I COLLECTED THE FACTS AS BEST AS I COULD. I STOOD MOTIONLESS, MY NERVES NEARLY FRAYED.

HERE, LESS THAN A FOOT AWAY FROM ME, WAS THE VERY MAN THAT KENNETH IRONS WARNED WOULD DO ANYTHING FOR THE WITCHBLADE...

...HE STALKED ME--HUNTED ME--AND CAUGHT IN HIS BARE HANDS THE THREE BULLETS I FIRED AT HIM.

IN A DISPLAY OF COMPETITIVE GRANDEUR, HE HAD PINNED ME AND DROPPED THE BULLETS UPON MY CHEST, TAKING PRIDE IN SHOWING THAT I COULDN'T DEFEND MYSELF AGAINST HIM.

SOON, WE WERE ON OUR FEET AGAIN. THIS MAN TOWERING ABOVE ME WITH A MARTINET'S COMPOSURE, THE SILENCE WAS BROKEN WHEN, IN A HUSHED GROWL THAT BELIED AN UTTERLY SOPHISTICATED ENGLISH DIALECT, HE SAID,"YOUR PERSEVERENCE IS INDEED ATTRACTIVE, MS. PEZZINI..."

WAS THIS BASTARD JUST PLAYING MIND GAMES WITH ME NOW? BACK ON LIBERTY ISLAND, HE SPOKE OF WANTING ME TO SUFFER. WELL, THAT LITTLE PLOY WAS GETTING REALLY OLD WITH ME.

SO WHILE HE WASTED HIS TIME GLARING DOWN ON ME WITH THAT SMUGNESS OF HIS, SEEMINGLY LOOKING FOR GLINTS OF FEAR IN MY EYES TO VALIDATE WHAT-EVER MACHO SHOWMANSHIP HE WAS DISPLAYING, I THOUGHT OF MY PLAN.

KICKING HIM IN THE GROIN HADN'T STOPPED HIM. PERHAPS THE EYES THIS TIME. THOSE GREY EYES.

I MONITORED EVERY SLIGHT MOVEMENT HE MADE. EVERY SHIFT IN STANCE. ANTICIPATING THE WORST. CLEARLY REMEMBERING THAT THIS MAN, DESPITE HIS AIR OF CALM, WAS STILL A MURDERER.

HIS AMBITION TO TAKE MY LIFE HAD BEEN AMONG MY MOST FRIGHTENING MOMENTS EVER. HAD IT NOT BEEN FOR KENNETH IRONS, I'M NOT SO SURE I'D BE ALIVE. IN FACT, I DOUBTED IT.

THEN I FELT HIS BODY TENSE SLIGHTLY. THIS WAS IT.

HE RAISED HIS OPEN HAND. I RECOILED, AS MY MUSCLES TIGHTENED AND MY HEART NEARLY *EXPLODED.*

NEVER DID I UNTENSE DURING HIS LITTLE *CONTROL SCHEME.* INSTEAD I MET HIS EYES, HOPING TO MAKE SOME PERSONAL CONNECTION THAT MIGHT'VE MADE IT MORE DIFFICULT FOR HIM TO HURT ME.

I FELT A STING OF *EMBARRASSMENT,* MY EYES STILL UNCONTROLLABLY FLINCHING, WHEN HIS HAND DIDN'T STRIKE ME AS EXPECTED. AGAIN, THIS GAME OF CONTROL. I COULD ONLY SPECULATE THAT HE *ENJOYED* TOYING WITH ME.

WHETHER BECAUSE OF MY EYE CONTACT OR SOME OTHER REASON WITHIN HIMSELF, HE BROKE THE SILENCE AGAIN-- WITH A DELUGE OF FACTS.

HE SPOKE OF HAVING A *NEED* TO TALK TO ME. HE BROUGHT UP LIBERTY ISLAND AND WAS FULL OF FRUSTRATING VAGARIES. HE JUST THREW THINGS OUT THERE WITHOUT PAUSE, NEVER WAITING FOR MY REBUTTAL. HE DIDN'T CARE. I FELT LIKE A *PRIEST* AT A MOBSTER'S CONFESSIONAL.

I LISTENED LIKE A COP, WAITING FOR THE LIES. BECAUSE IN OUR BUSINESS, EVERYBODY LIES.

HE SPOKE OF THE DREAM HE HAD AND SURREALISTICALLY I LISTENED WHILE HE RECOUNTED *EVERYTHING* I HAD DREAMT.

THE RIVERDALE COMPOUND. HOME OF THE CHURCH OF HOLY PROSPERITY. 11:40 P.M.

I NEVER THOUGHT I'D STEP FOOT IN THIS PLACE. FOR SOME REASON, I'VE ALWAYS STAYED AWAY FROM RELIGIONS THAT BASE THEIR FOUNDATION ON CLEVER SLOGANS LIKE, "YOUR SPIRIT IS *OUR* BUSINESS."

MAYBE IT'S ME, BUT A BELIEF IN GOD SHOULDN'T BE BASED ON HOW MUCH MONEY YOU HAVE. THAT'S JUST MY OPINION.

BUT IF BEING HERE WITH KEN HELPS RAISE MONEY FOR A CURE FOR CANCER--I CAN CERTAINLY PUT AWAY MY DIFFERENCES. IN FACT, IT'LL BE A GOOD CHANGE OF SCENERY.

...MR IRONS, WE'RE QUITE INSPIRED THAT YOU COULD MAKE OUR BENEFIT TONIGHT.

YES, ALL THE FELLOW *PROSPERITES* HAVE FOUND YOUR APPEARANCE QUITE INSPIRATIONAL.

OF COURSE, MY FRIENDS, AFTER PERUSING YOUR RECENT *RESEARCH*, I BELIEVE YOUR THEORIES ON CANCER TO BE *REFRESHING*.

WHY, I'M FLATTERED, MR. IR--

PARDON ME...

...BUT I BELIEVE MY GUEST HAS *ARRIVED*.

THAT GAUNTLET FORSOOK HER LONG AGO.

I'M SORRY--OR WERE THERE TOO MANY OTHER THOUGHTS RACING THROUGH THAT COMPLEX MIND OF YOURS? YOUR PARTNER, MICHAEL YEE, PERHAPS? WHAT WITH HIS UNTIMELY AND INCONVENIENT DEATH, IT'S NO WONDER!

PERHAPS THERE WAS MORE, TOO. I DON'T BLAME YOU FOR SLIPPING UP, SARA. IT WAS SURELY A SHOCK TO YOUR SYSTEM--THE DISASTER AT THE RIALTO, YOUR KID-NAPPING FROM THE GYM-- MAYBE TRYING TO RESURRECT MICHAEL WAS A LITTLE MORE THAN YOU SHOULD HAVE ATTEMPTED.

SHE KNOWS SHE MUST DEAL WITH THIS ON HER OWN--WITHOUT THE WITCHBLADE.

COULD NOT A CLEVER DETECTIVE LIKE YOURSELF REALIZE THAT THE SLIP FROM WHICH MY YACHT WAS DOCKED, WAS INDEED REGISTERED UNDER MY NAME?

I DO THINK MANY OF YOUR COLLEAGUES COULD LEARN FROM YOUR CARELESS-NESS.

SHE WANTED QUICK ANSWERS--AN EASY RESOLUTION.

SHE EVEN BELIEVED, FOR A FLEETING MOMENT, THAT SHE COULD LIVE THE GLAMOROUS LIFESTYLE SHE ONCE LONGED FOR.

NOW SHE'S ALONE.

SARA, DO YOU REALLY THINK I JUST HAPPENED TO STUMBLE UPON YOU AT LIBERTY ISLAND?

CAITY TOWER CENTRAL PARK WEST, NEW YORK: 4:25 A.M.

FRUSTRATION.

A STABBING, HOT, AGONIZING FRUSTRATION.

JUST TOO MANY EVENTS, ONE RIGHT AFTER ANOTHER, LEADING TO THIS-- THE PINNACLE OF DESPAIR AND FUTILITY--WHEN EVERYTHING COULD HAVE

IT IS ALWAYS DARKEST BEFORE SUNRISE.

WITH SWEET STRENGTH, WITH NEW VISION, SHE SPEAKS TO THE GOLDEN MYSTERY OF DAWN AND TO THE WORLD.

I AM THE LIGHT.

AN ANGEL OF LIFE.

I AM POWER.

I AM MORE THAN HE THOUGHT I'D BE.

S-SARA?

WHEN I WAS A LITTLE GIRL I WISHED I HAD THE POWER TO PREVENT BAD PEOPLE FROM HURTING ANYONE.

WITHOUT THE WITCHBLADE, IT'S JUST MY JOB.

BUT WITH IT, I HAVE THE ABILITY TO SAVE OTHERS BEYOND AN INCONCEIVABLE CAPACITY.

THE ONLY DIFFERENCE IS—I'M NOT AFRAID ANYMORE.

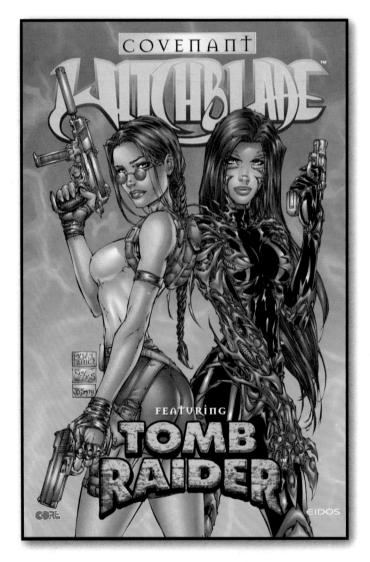